W9-AYF-763

Canadian Curriculum SummerSmart 1·2

Olivia.

Credits

Photos (Front Cover "children" Gennadiy Poznyakov/123RF.com, "beach toys" serezniy/123RF.com, "beach" Alexandr Ozerov/123RF.com. Back Cover "children" Anatoliy Samara/123RF.com, "school bus" Thomas Bedenk/123RF.com, "children" Dmitriy Shironosov/123RF.com, "classroom" Franck Boston/123RF.com, "girl looking at grass" Sergiy Bykhunenko/123RF.com, "girl blowing windmill" Logos/123RF.com, "bee" szefei/123RF.com, "lorikeets" Tyler Panian/123RF.com, "children" Anatoliy Samara/123RF.com, "Chateau Frontenac" Susan Peterson/123RF.com)

Copyright © 2015 Popular Book Company (Canada) Limited

Printed in China

ISBN: 978-1-77149-143-3

English

Mathematics

Science

Social Studies

Arts & Crafts

Contents

Grades 1-2

Week

ISBN: 978-1-77149-143-3

Week

ISBN: 978-1-77149-143-3

Dear Parent:

While all work and no play makes Jack a dull boy, all play and no work would probably make Jack forget most of what he has learned, which is why it is necessary to schedule regular practice in the long summer vacation to help your child consolidate what he or she has learned.

This is where Canadian Curriculum SummerSmart can help.

Canadian Curriculum SummerSmart provides practice for your child to review the essentials taught in the previous academic year and prepares him or her for the grade ahead with confidence. The series is organized in an easy-to-use format: each title is made up of eight weeks (units) of work so your child can complete one unit each week during the summer vacation. The units are comprised of practice in English, Math, Science, and Social Studies. Engaging Arts and Crafts activities, as well as Comics and Fun Places to Go in Summer, are also included for added fun.

Your child will be delighted to have Canadian Curriculum SummerSmart as his or her summer learning buddy.

Your Partner in Education,
Popular Book Company (Canada) Limited

ISBN: 978-1-77149-143-3

WEEK 1

English

- read a poem and match rhyming words
- put words in alphabetical order
- do a word search
- write a paragraph

Mathematics

- do the counting
- find the total value of coins
- identify symmetrical figures
- put events in order
- read a pictograph

Science

- learn about the five senses
- complete poems about senses

Social Studies

- explore your family tree

* The Canadian penny is no longer in circulation. It is used in the unit to show money amounts to the cent.

ISBN: 978-1-77149-143-3

A. Read the poem. Then write the words in bold that rhyme with the given ones below.

Summer Fun

The **school** doors **flew** open.

We all rushed out.

It's summer vacation.

We began to shout!

Swimming, biking, playing with **friends**.

Our **days** will be **fun**-filled **till** summer's **end**.

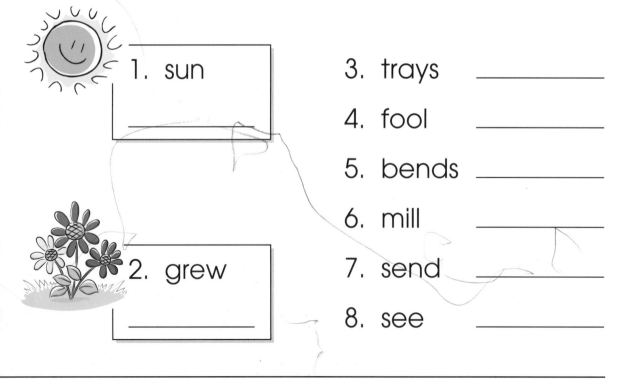

1. sun _____

2. grew _____

3. trays _____

4. fool _____

5. bends _____

6. mill _____

7. send _____

8. see _____

ISBN: 978-1-77149-143-3

B. Read the list of summer activities. Place the words in alphabetical order.

swimming

soccer

biking

hiking

baseball

tennis

fishing

rollerblading

camping

boating

1. _____

2. _____

3. _____

4. _____

5. _____

6. _____

7. _____

8. _____

9. _____

10. _____

ISBN: 978-1-77149-143-3

C. Circle the words from (B) in the word search.

English

b	u	s	s	o	c	c	e	r	g	s	r
i	e	t	w	j	l	r	c	l	e	m	o
k	h	f	i	s	h	i	n	g	p	q	l
i	g	j	m	b	a	s	e	b	a	l	l
n	i	o	m	v	i	p	a	l	r	s	e
g	q	i	i	e	j	o	s	c	h	s	r
t	e	n	n	i	s	u	d	a	z	d	b
p	k	v	g	l	e	y	f	m	x	f	l
r	h	s	e	p	q	t	g	p	c	g	a
t	f	t	u	t	a	r	j	i	v	y	d
h	i	k	i	n	g	e	k	n	b	k	i
y	w	k	s	o	c	w	l	g	n	o	n
c	d	b	o	a	t	i	n	g	m	v	g

ISBN: 978-1-77149-143-3

D. Read the paragraph. Then write a paragraph about something that you enjoy doing during the summer. Draw a picture to go with your paragraph.

A paragraph is a group of sentences about one main idea.

Example

I enjoy biking. It is good exercise. I like to look at the trees, flowers, and birds along the way. Maybe this summer, I will see some interesting animals too!

My Paragraph

ISBN: 978-1-77149-143-3

A. Count and write how many things are in each group. Then fill in the blanks.

1.

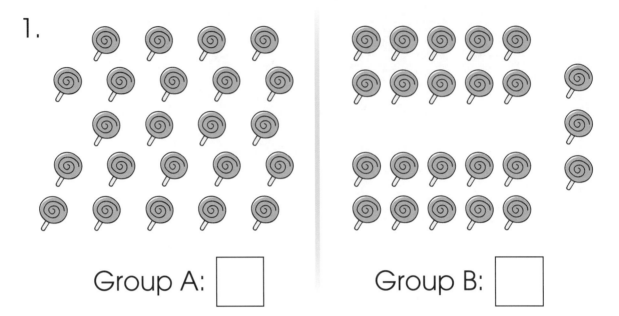

Group A: ☐   Group B: ☐

Group ____ is easier to count.

2.

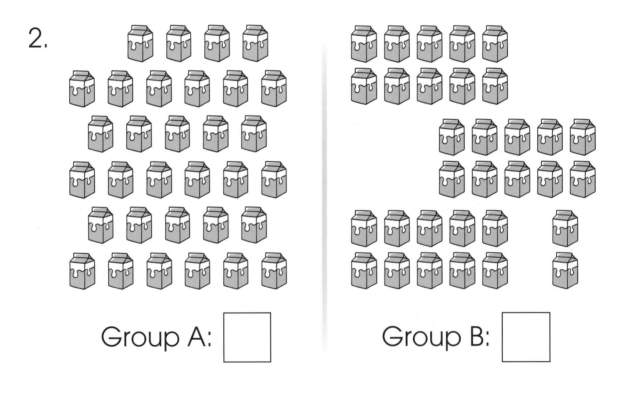

Group A: ☐   Group B: ☐

Group ____ is easier to count.

ISBN: 978-1-77149-143-3

B. Gary shows the cost of each item with coins. Write the costs. Then solve the problems.

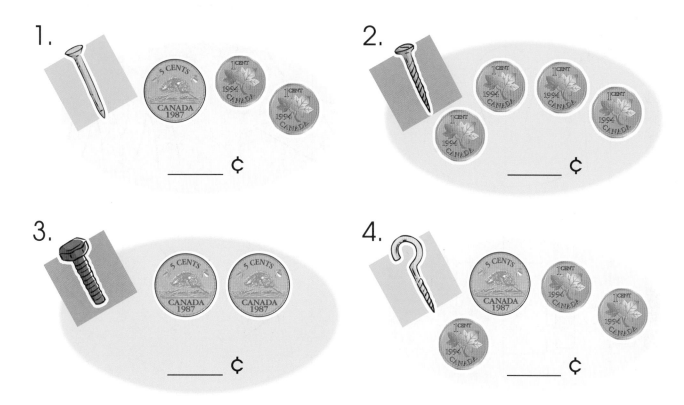

1. _____ ¢

2. _____ ¢

3. _____ ¢

4. _____ ¢

5. 1 hinge needs 6 screws. How many screws are needed for 2 hinges?

_____ = _____

_____ screws are needed.

6. Gary has 7 nails in the drawer and 8 nails in the box. How many nails does he have in all?

_____ = _____

He has _____ nails in all.

ISBN: 978-1-77149-143-3   *Grades 1-2*

C. Colour the logos that are symmetrical.

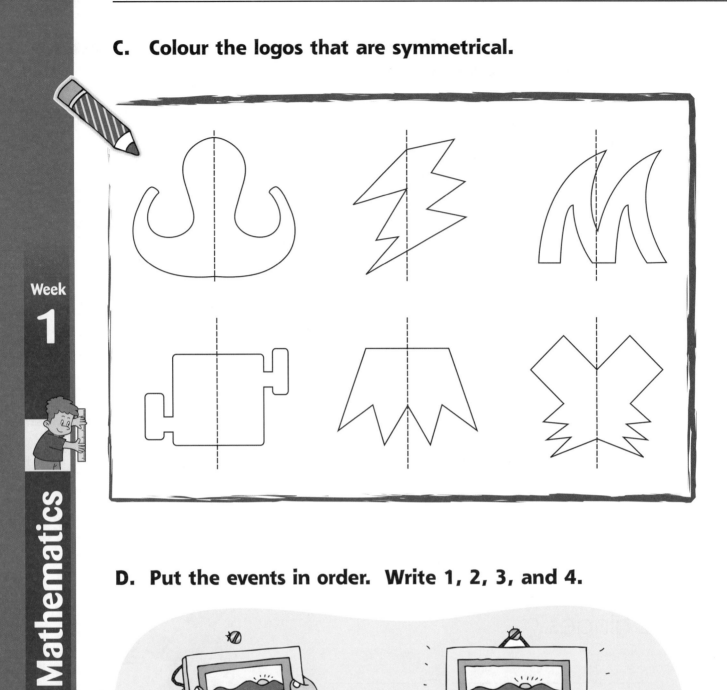

D. Put the events in order. Write 1, 2, 3, and 4.

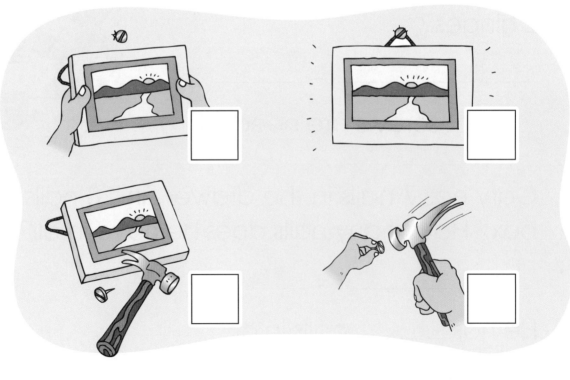

ISBN: 978-1-77149-143-3

E. **Gary uses a graph to show how many photos he took last week. Look at the graph. Then fill in the blanks.**

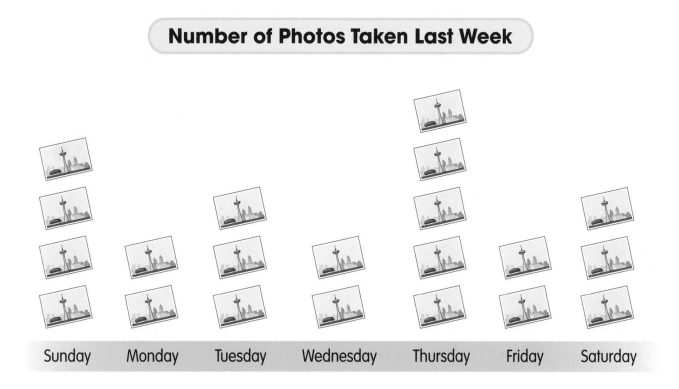

Number of Photos Taken Last Week

1. On Wednesday, Gary took _____ photos.

2. From Monday to Friday, Gary took _____ photos in all.

3. Gary took 4 photos on _____ .

4. Gary took the most photos on _____ .

5. Gary took _____ more photos on Thursday than he did on Wednesday.

6. Gary took _____ photos in all.

ISBN: 978-1-77149-143-3

A. We have five senses. Draw lines to match the objects with the senses.

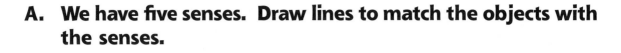

Week

1

Science

hearing

smell

touch

taste

sight

Science Fun

Many bats are nearly blind. They use their sense of hearing to "see"!

ISBN: 978-1-77149-143-3

B. Complete the poems by using "sense" words.

Is it mashed potatoes,
Porridge or paste?
I know it by

My Sense of

1. _____

There! In the sky!
A plane or a kite?
I know it by

My Sense of

2. _____

Skunk or flower?
It's easy to tell.
I know it by

My Sense of

3. _____

A haircut. What's left?
I say, "Not much!"
I know it by

My Sense of

4. _____

The band is playing.
The crowd is cheering.
I know it by

My Sense of

5. _____

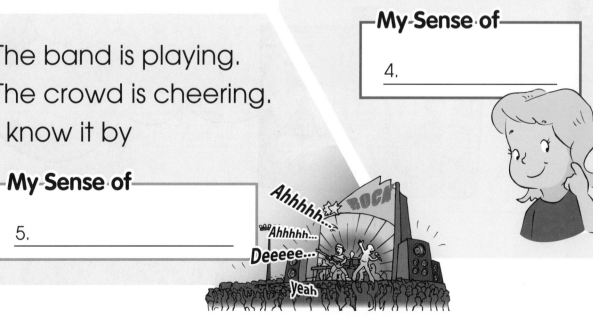

15

ISBN: 978-1-77149-143-3

Draw or paste pictures of you and your family members on the tree.

Social Studies

ISBN: 978-1-77149-143-3

Names

My grandparents

My parents

Me

My brother(s)

My sister(s)

I like your family tree!

ISBN: 978-1-77149-143-3

ISBN: 978-1-77149-143-3

WEEK 2

English

- read a sign and answer questions
- categorize words
- add punctuation marks to sentences
- correct wrong consonants

Mathematics

- name and count shapes
- draw a picture using shapes
- learn comparative words

Science

- learn about where animals build their homes
- complete a crossword puzzle

Social Studies

- learn about celebrations around the world
- draw and write about your family's special celebration

ISBN: 978-1-77149-143-3

A. Read the sign. Then give short answers to the questions.

GARAGE SALE

Date: Saturday, July 1
Sunday, July 2

Time: 9:00 a.m. to 3:00 p.m.

Items: toys, clothes, furniture,
comic books

1. What time does the garage sale begin?

   _____

2. What time does the garage sale end?

   _____

3. On which days will the sale be held?

   _____

4. What kinds of things can you buy at the garage sale?

   _____

ISBN: 978-1-77149-143-3

B. Here is a list of things sold at the garage sale. Read the list and put each word or phrase in the correct box.

Garage Sale

pants   chair   coat   dress   hat

doll   desk   teddy bear   couch

scarf   table   baseball   skipping rope

bed   jigsaw puzzle

Furniture

_____

_____

_____

_____

_____

Toy

_____

_____

_____

_____

Clothing

_____

_____

_____

_____

_____

ISBN: 978-1-77149-143-3   *Grades 1-2*

C. Add ".", "!", or "?" to what the children say at the garage sale.

1.

I like the skipping rope ☐

You can have it for a dollar ☐

2.

Can I take it home ☐

Of course ☐

3.

Be careful ☐

English

ISBN: 978-1-77149-143-3

**D. Look at each picture and read the words. One consonant is
wrong. Correct and rewrite each word.**

puck

_ _ _ _

pat

_ _ _

cut

_ _ _

look

_ _ _ _

ramp

_ _ _ _

big

_ _ _

bite

_ _ _ _

fun

_ _ _

fair

_ _ _ _

hike

_ _ _ _

ISBN: 978-1-77149-143-3

A. Simon has cut out some shapes from a cardboard. Help him name the shapes.

> circle   triangle   rectangle   square

A *square*

B *triangle*

C *rectangle*

D *rectangle*

E *circle*

F *triangle*

B. Look at Simon's picture. Help him count and write the number of each shape.

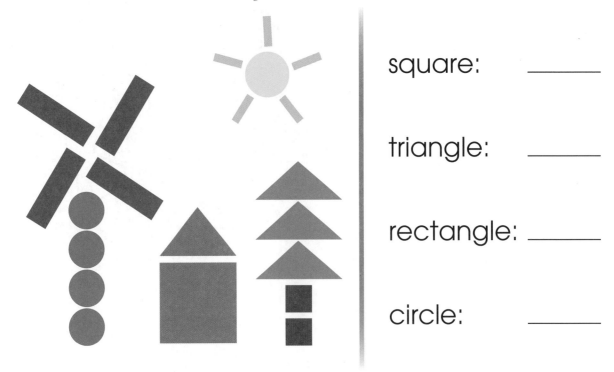

square: _____

triangle: _____

rectangle: _____

circle: _____

ISBN: 978-1-77149-143-3

Mathematics

C. Draw and name the shape you get when you trace each object on paper.

1.

Shape: circle

2.

Shape:

triangle

3.

4.

Shape:

square

Shape:

rectangle

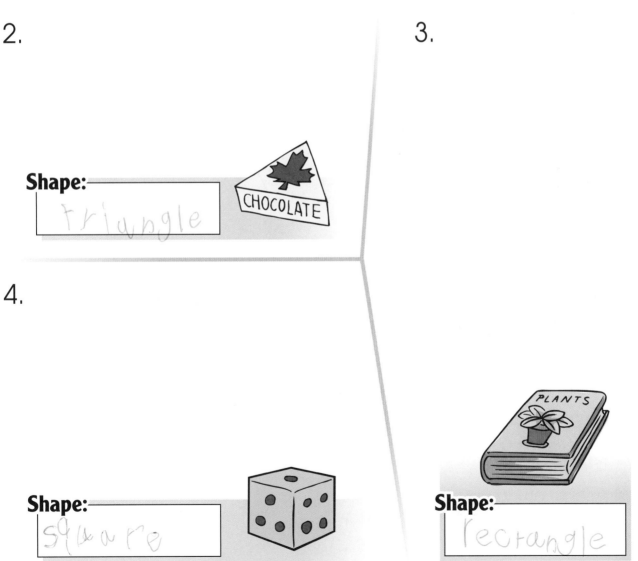

25

ISBN: 978-1-77149-143-3

D. Follow the instructions to complete the picture.

Steps to Draw Your Flower

- stalk: draw a long rectangle under the circle
- petals: draw 8 small circles around the circle
- leaves: draw a triangle on both sides of the rectangle

Draw a happy face on the big circle and colour your flower.

Mathematics

ISBN: 978-1-77149-143-3

E. Compare the shapes. Circle the correct words or letters to complete the sentences.

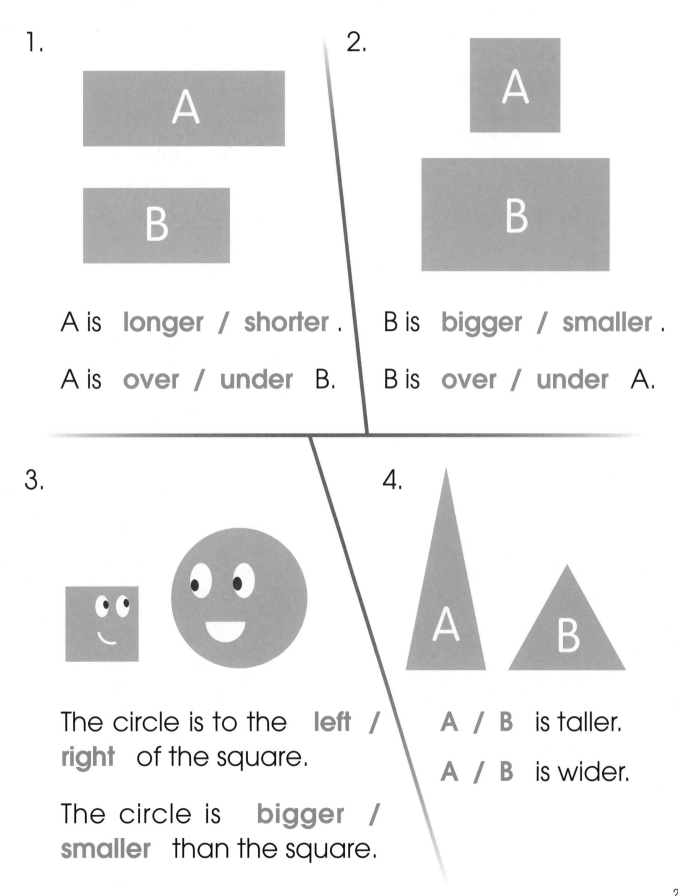

1.

A is **longer** / **shorter** .

A is **over** / **under** B.

2.

B is **bigger** / **smaller** .

B is **over** / **under** A.

3.

The circle is to the **left** / **right** of the square.

The circle is **bigger** / **smaller** than the square.

4.

A / **B** is taller.

A / **B** is wider.

ISBN: 978-1-77149-143-3

A. **Where do these animals make their homes? Write the names of the animals in the environment in which they live.**

Animal Homes

fox   shrimp
bird   bear
squirrel   fish

In the forest

_____

_____

In the river

_____

_____

In the tree

_____

_____

ISBN: 978-1-77149-143-3

B. **We have special names for different animals' homes. Use the clues to complete the puzzle with the given words.**

Sometimes animals make their homes in other animals' homes. Hermit crabs look for empty shells. A cuckoo bird lays her eggs in other birds' nests.

NEST   DEN   LODGE   WEB   HIVE   SHELL

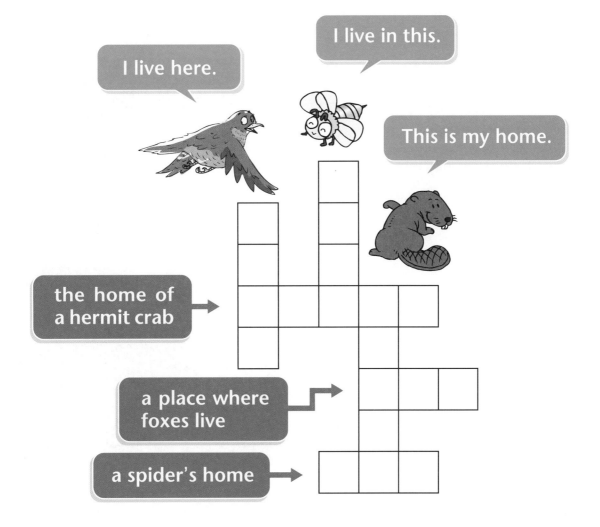

I live here.

I live in this.

This is my home.

the home of a hermit crab

a place where foxes live

a spider's home

ISBN: 978-1-77149-143-3

A. Match the celebrations.

> People from different cultures have their own interesting celebrations and festivals.

Eid ul-Fitr
Muslim celebration

Hanukkah
Jewish holiday

Powwow
First Nations celebration

Social Studies

ISBN: 978-1-77149-143-3

B. Draw or paste a picture of your family's special celebration. Then write about it.

My family's special celebration:

_____

We celebrate it on: _____

Special foods we eat: _____

 I like it because _____

_____

31

ISBN: 978-1-77149-143-3

ISBN: 978-1-77149-143-3

WEEK 3

English
- read a story and answer questions
- put sentences in order
- write compound words
- solve riddles

Mathematics
- name solids
- use position words
- classify shapes according to their attributes
- recognize patterns

Science
- identify natural and human-made structures
- learn about the functions of structures

Social Studies
- learn about the traditional foods of different countries
- describe how you celebrate Canadian festivals

ISBN: 978-1-77149-143-3

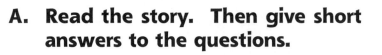

Bob's
Bird Bath

Bob was so excited. He found a treasure at his neighbour's garage sale. It was an old bird bath. It cost only $1. Bob bought the bird bath and placed it outside in his backyard. He then took the garden hose and filled the bath with water. As the afternoon sun warmed the water, Bob watched robins, bluebirds, and cardinals enjoy the bird bath.

1. Where did Bob get the bird bath?

   _____

2. How much was the bird bath?

   _____

3. Where did Bob put his bird bath?

   _____

4. What kinds of birds visited Bob's bird bath?

   _____

ISBN: 978-1-77149-143-3

Week 3

A

English

B. Read the five sentences. Rewrite them in the correct order.

- Bob bought the bird bath.
- The sun warmed the water.
- Bob found a treasure.
- He filled the bath with water.
- Bob put the bird bath in the backyard.

1. _____

2. _____

3. _____

4. _____

5. _____

C. Read the story again. Find four compound words and write them on the lines below.

1. _____

2. _____

3. _____

4. _____

ISBN: 978-1-77149-143-3

D. Complete the compound words.

paper	fish	melon	board
cake	box	ball	fly

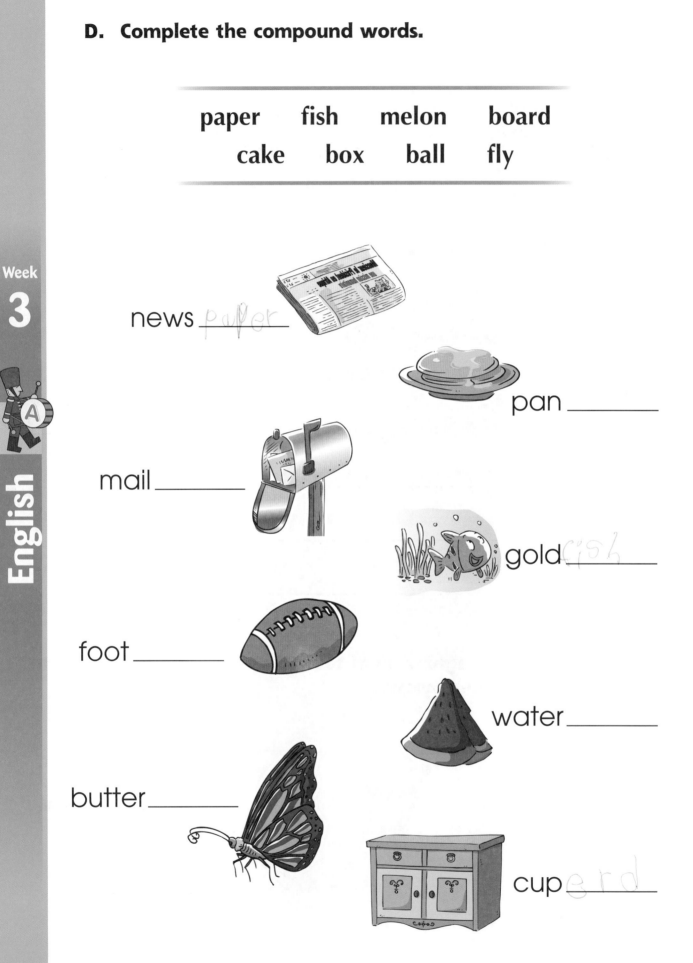

news _paper_

pan _____

mail _____

gold _fish_

foot _____

water _____

butter _____

cup _erd_

ISBN: 978-1-77149-143-3

E. Use the code to solve the riddles.

Secret Code

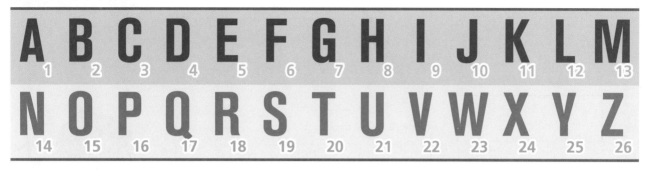

A B C D E F G H I J K L M
1 2 3 4 5 6 7 8 9 10 11 12 13

N O P Q R S T U V W X Y Z
14 15 16 17 18 19 20 21 22 23 24 25 26

1.

What bird is always at the dining table?

$\overline{}_{1}$ $\overline{}_{19}$ $\overline{}_{23}$ $\overline{}_{1}$ $\overline{}_{12}$ $\overline{}_{12}$ $\overline{}_{15}$ $\overline{}_{23}$

2.

What does a duck eat with its soup?

$\overline{}_{3}$ $\overline{}_{18}$ $\overline{}_{1}$ $\overline{}_{3}$ $\overline{}_{11}$ $\overline{}_{5}$ $\overline{}_{18}$ $\overline{}_{19}$

3. What bird is always sad?

$\overline{}_{1}$ $\overline{}_{2}$ $\overline{}_{12}$ $\overline{}_{21}$ $\overline{}_{5}$ $\overline{}_{2}$ $\overline{}_{9}$ $\overline{}_{18}$ $\overline{}_{4}$

ISBN: 978-1-77149-143-3

A. Look at the solids. Write the names of the shapes in the boxes.

cylinder   sphere   cube   cone

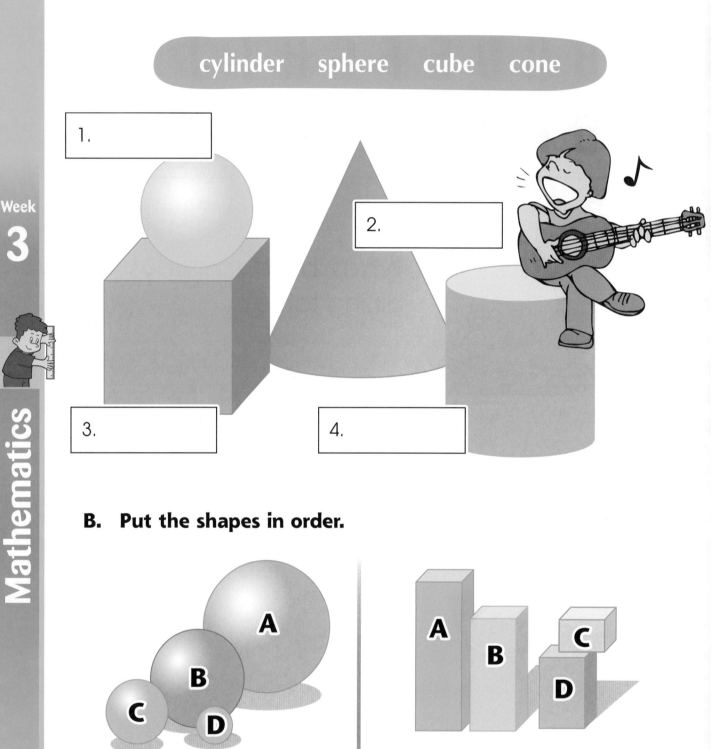

1.

2.

3.

4.

B. Put the shapes in order.

smallest   biggest   tallest   shortest

ISBN: 978-1-77149-143-3

C. Look at each group of shapes. Complete the sentences with the given words.

in front of	**between**	**on**
under	**over**	**behind**
	beside	**inside**

1. The cylinders are _____ the cube.

    The cone is _____ the cube.

    The sphere is _____ the cylinders.

2. The sphere is _____ the box.

    The cube is _____ the box.

    The cube is _____ the cylinder.

3. The cylinder is _____ the sphere.

    The sphere is _____ the cubes.

    The cone is _____ the sphere.

39

ISBN: 978-1-77149-143-3

D. Read what the children say and colour the shapes.

1.

Colour the shapes that can roll.

2.

Colour the shapes that can be stacked up.

ISBN: 978-1-77149-143-3

E. Check ✔ the shapes that are cut into halves.

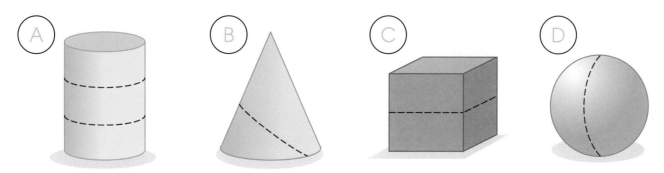

F. Follow the pattern and colour the shape that comes next in each group. Then circle the correct word to complete what the girl says.

1.

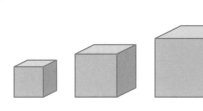 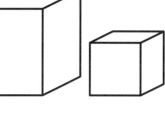

> The size of the cubes is getting
> smaller / bigger   .

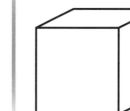

2.

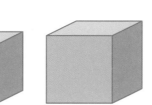

> The height of the cones is getting
> higher / lower   .

ISBN: 978-1-77149-143-3

A. Draw lines to show whether each structure is natural or human-made.

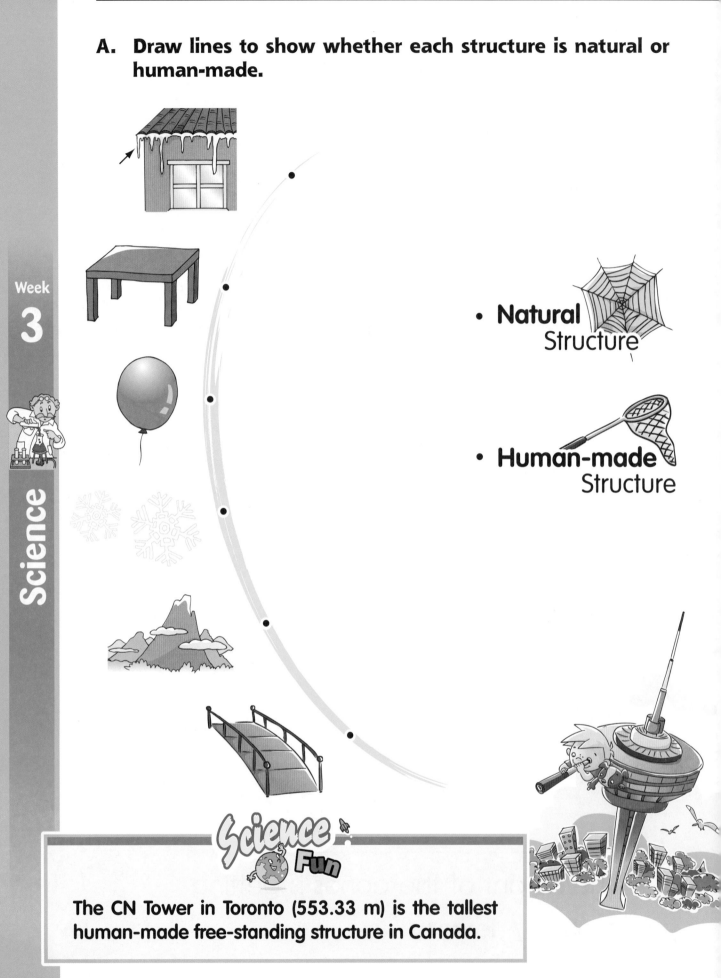

Natural Structure

Human-made Structure

Science Fun

The CN Tower in Toronto (553.33 m) is the tallest human-made free-standing structure in Canada.

ISBN: 978-1-77149-143-3

B. Some structures are built for purposes other than giving shelter. Match to show the functions of the structures.

Some structures might have more than one function.

Functions of
Structures

- to give protection

- to support a load

- to span a distance

43

ISBN: 978-1-77149-143-3   *Grades 1-2*

A. **Different countries have their own traditional foods to celebrate their festivals. Fill in the blanks.**

Country: India   China
Food: samosas   turnip cakes

1. **Lunar New Year**

Food

Country: _____

2. **Diwali**

Food

Country: _____

ISBN: 978-1-77149-143-3

B. Look at the celebrations in Canada. Draw or paste pictures of the foods that we usually have on these special days. Then write about them.

Canada Day

Food

Things to do: _____

_____

Thanksgiving Day

Food

Things to do: _____

_____

ISBN: 978-1-77149-143-3

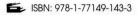 ISBN: 978-1-77149-143-3

Arts & Crafts
- create a picture with your thumb

Comics
- The Mouse-Deer's Trick

Fun Places to Go in Summer
- Centre Island

ISBN: 978-1-77149-143-3

Paint with your Thumb

Arts & Crafts

Materials:

- white paper
- paint on paper plates
- markers

Lay out a newspaper or plastic sheet on your work area.

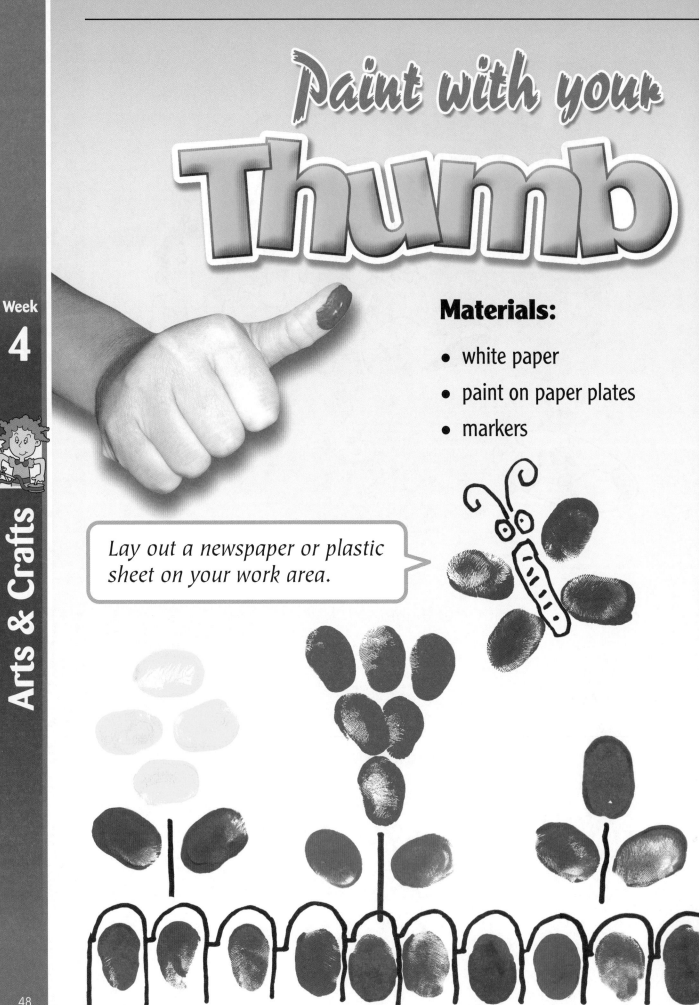

ISBN: 978-1-77149-143-3

Directions:

1. Pour 1 tablespoon of dry paint onto each paper plate.

2. Pour 1 tablespoon of water into paint and mix.

3. Press your thumb into paint. Wipe off the excess.

4. "Paint" a picture.

5. Add details with markers.

ISBN: 978-1-77149-143-3

49

The Mouse-Deer's Trick

Once there was an old tiger.
He lived in a big forest.

Every day, he would try to catch other animals by the salt lick.

The other animals were troubled.
They needed salt to stay healthy.

This is bad.

ISBN: 978-1-77149-143-3

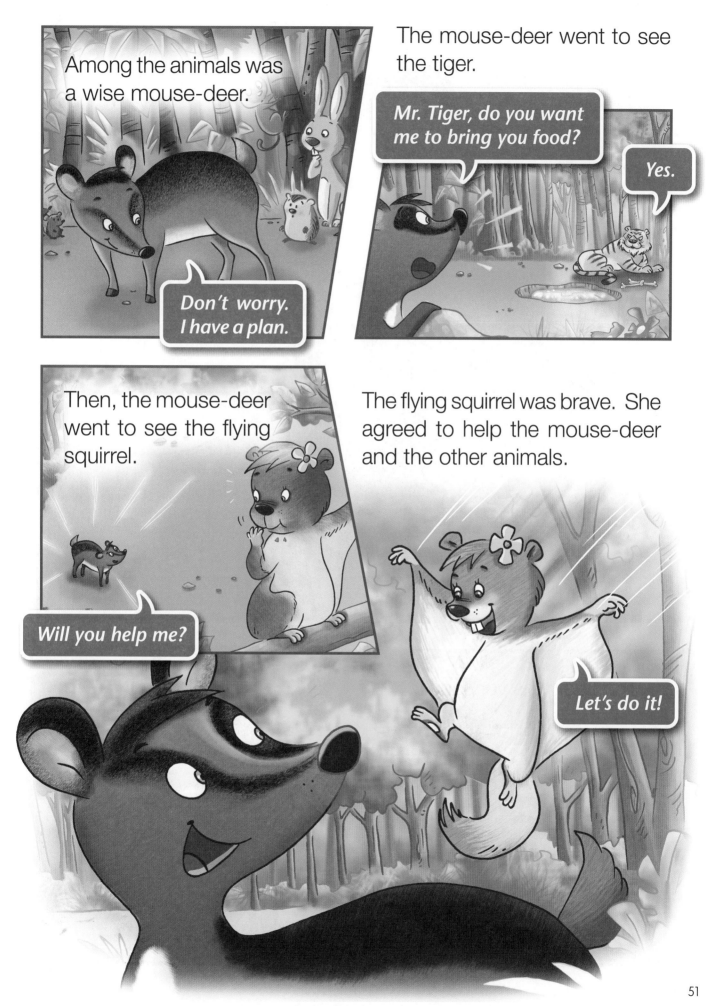

ISBN: 978-1-77149-143-3

The mouse-deer and the flying squirrel went to see the tiger. They told him that the food was stolen by a fat, old tiger with a flying squirrel sitting on his nose.

...He was mean.

The tiger was very angry.

Take me to him!

Sure! I'll lead you there.

ISBN: 978-1-77149-143-3

ISBN: 978-1-77149-143-3

Grades 1-2

Centre Island

A short ferry ride from downtown Toronto, Ontario takes you to Centre Island, where you can have lots of summer fun in the sun.

On Centre Island, you can swim at a sandy beach, run through a hedge maze, or simply bike, rollerblade, or stroll around the island. When you are tired and hungry, you can have a picnic under the shade of some trees with your family. If you fancy something more exciting, there is an amusement park for kids your age with fun rides, like a carousel, a Ferris wheel, a rocking ferry, and a swan ride.

Hop on a ferry, get away from the city, and have another day filled with laughter this summer!

ISBN: 978-1-77149-143-3

WEEK 5

Week 5

English
- complete a story
- find sentences that do not belong
- write sentences
- recognize consonant blends

Mathematics
- solve probability problems
- do addition and subtraction
- follow number patterns
- identify shapes

Science
- relate objects to the materials from which they are made
- learn about energy

Social Studies
- label the globe
- learn about the world map

ISBN: 978-1-77149-143-3

A. Read the story. Then fill in the blanks with the words from the word bank.

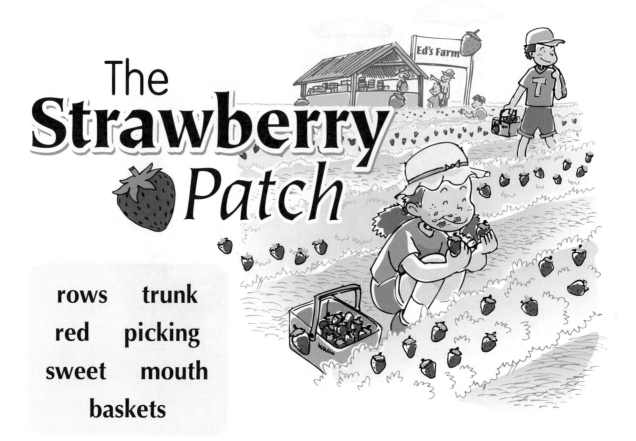

The
Strawberry
Patch

rows   trunk
red   picking
sweet   mouth
baskets

Jan, Ted, and Aunt Mary were going strawberry 1._____ . They put four empty 2._____ into the 3._____ of the car and left for the strawberry patch.

The children were thrilled when they saw the 4._____ of strawberries. Jan picked one big, 5._____ berry and popped it into her 6._____ . It was so very juicy and 7._____ .

ISBN: 978-1-77149-143-3

B. **Read each group of sentences. Draw a line through the sentence that does not belong.**

1. The patch was covered with strawberries. Jan picked two baskets of strawberries. There was a robin in the sky.

2. Strawberry picking is fun. Jan and Ted enjoy riding their bikes with Aunt Mary. You can eat as you pick.

3. I like strawberries. They taste sweet and they smell good. We can make strawberry jam too. Grapes are purple in colour.

4. The strawberry patch was up north. Cherries are red too. It took us two hours to drive there.

5. I can make baskets. Ted's basket is very big. He fills it with strawberries.

ISBN: 978-1-77149-143-3   *Grades 1-2*

C. Decorate the welcome sign for the farm. Then write three sentences about the children and Aunt Mary's trip to the farm.

_____

_____

_____

_____

ISBN: 978-1-77149-143-3

D. Say what each picture is. Circle the consonant blend the word has. Then write the word on the line.

skates   flower   grapes   clown

plane   star   flag   spider

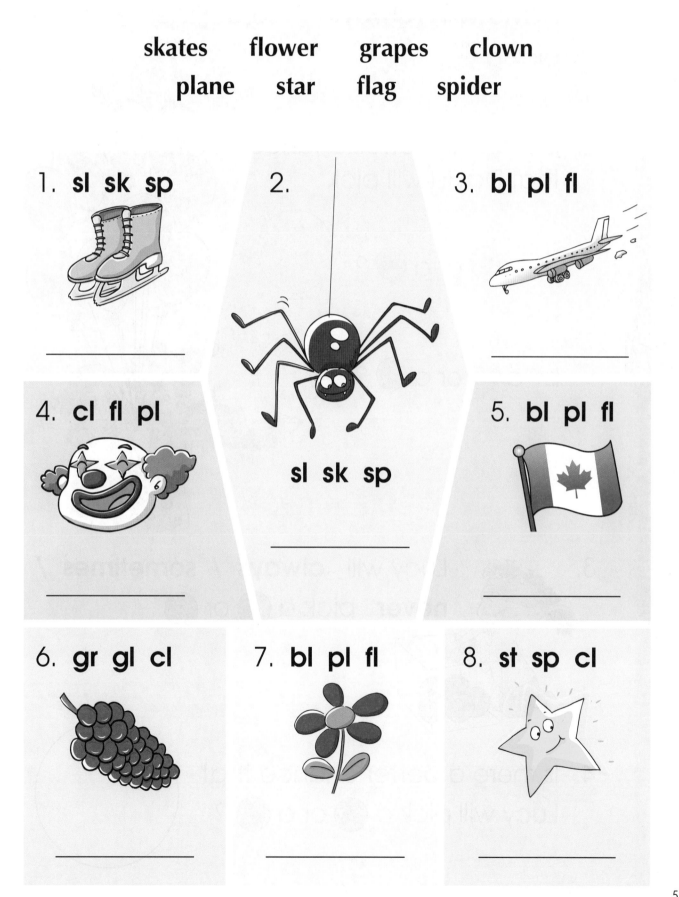

1. **sl sk sp**

2.

3. **bl pl fl**

4. **cl fl pl**

sl sk sp

5. **bl pl fl**

6. **gr gl cl**

7. **bl pl fl**

8. **st sp cl**

ISBN: 978-1-77149-143-3

A. Circle or draw the correct answers.

1. David will   **always / sometimes / never**
   pick a  .

2. Is there a better chance
   that David will pick

   a. a ⭐ or a 💜 ?

   b. a 💜 or a ⚪ ?

3.   Lucy will   **always / sometimes /
     never**   pick a ⭐ or ⚫ .

4. Is there a better chance that
   Lucy will pick a ⭐ or a ⚫ ?

ISBN: 978-1-77149-143-3

B. Solve the problems.

1. There are 6 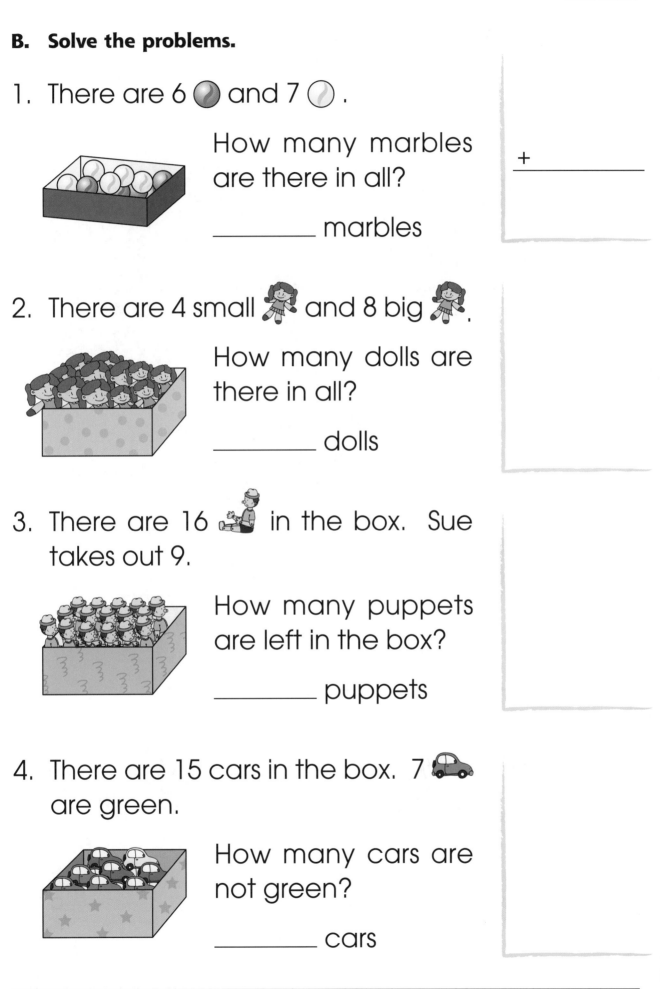 and 7 ◯ .

   How many marbles are there in all?

   _____ marbles

   + _____

2. There are 4 small 👧 and 8 big 👧.

   How many dolls are there in all?

   _____ dolls

3. There are 16 🧸 in the box. Sue takes out 9.

   How many puppets are left in the box?

   _____ puppets

4. There are 15 cars in the box. 7 🚗 are green.

   How many cars are not green?

   _____ cars

ISBN: 978-1-77149-143-3

C. Write the numbers in the boxes to show the number of each kind of animal at the zoo.

3 ones

5 tens

4 tens 2 ones

7 tens 9 ones

D. Fill in the missing numbers.

1. 42 44   48   54   58

2. 35 40   55   65

ISBN: 978-1-77149-143-3

Week **5**

Mathematics

E. **The shapes are made with different coloured wires. Name and count the shapes.**

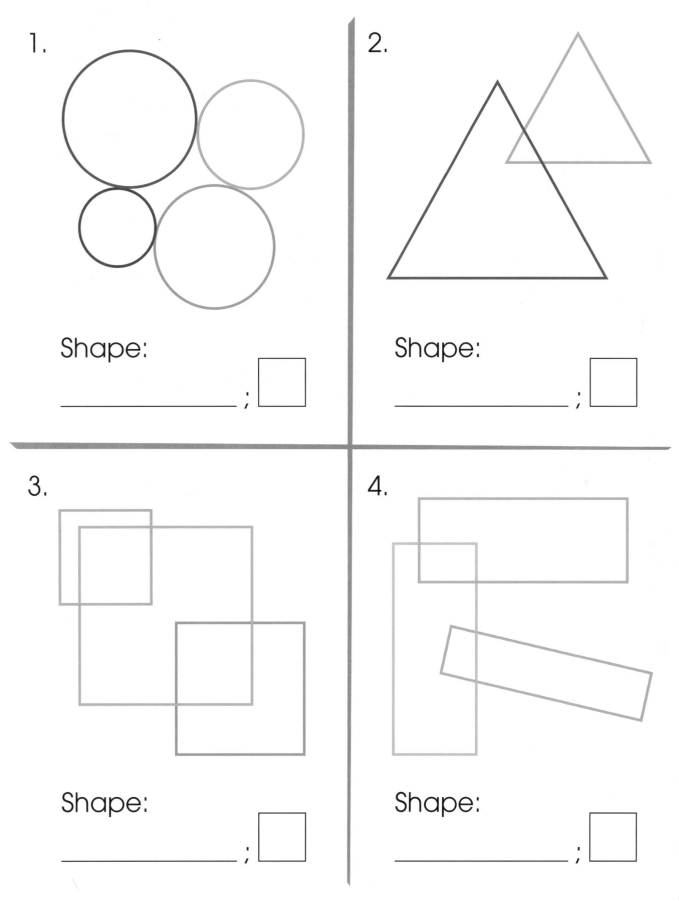

1.

Shape:

_____ ; ☐

2.

Shape:

_____ ; ☐

3.

Shape:

_____ ; ☐

4.

Shape:

_____ ; ☐

63

ISBN: 978-1-77149-143-3

A. Match each object with the material it is made of.

> *Objects that we use are made of materials with different properties.*

Objects

Materials

iron	cloth	glass
_____	_____	_____

feather	wood
_____	_____

ISBN: 978-1-77149-143-3

B. **The children show you how energy is used. Fill in the blanks to complete what they say.**

grow   change   think   move

1.

It takes energy to _____ .

It takes energy to _____ .

2.

It takes energy to _____ .

It takes energy to _____ .

ISBN: 978-1-77149-143-3

A. **Trace the equator with a red coloured pencil. Then fill in the blanks to label the globe and answer the questions.**

North   South

1.

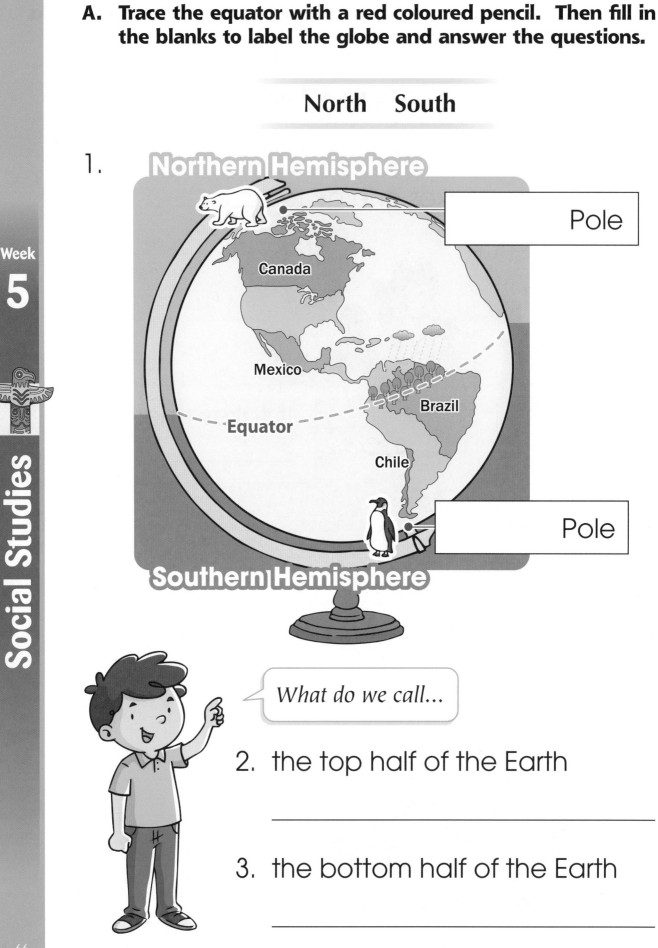

Week
5

Social Studies

Northern Hemisphere

Pole

Canada

Mexico

Brazil

Equator

Chile

Pole

Southern Hemisphere

What do we call...

2. the top half of the Earth

_____

3. the bottom half of the Earth

_____

ISBN: 978-1-77149-143-3

B. Look at the world map. Trace the equator with a red coloured pencil. Then answer the question and fill in the blanks.

The Seven Continents

_____

_____

_____

_____

_____

_____

_____

The Five Oceans

_____

_____

_____

_____

_____

The **World Map**

Arctic Ocean

Europe

Asia

Pacific Ocean

North America

Atlantic Ocean

Africa

Indian Ocean

Australia

Equator

South America

Pacific Ocean

Southern Ocean

Antarctica

N
W E
S

Which continent is Canada located on?

_____

ISBN: 978-1-77149-143-3

ISBN: 978-1-77149-143-3

WEEK 6

English

- read a story
- learn about camping items
- identify antonyms
- complete a word search

Mathematics

- compare capacities of containers
- solve problems about capacity
- identify shapes on solids

Science

- identify solids and liquids
- learn that water melts and freezes

Social Studies

- learn about different types of homes
- learn about different types of sports

ISBN: 978-1-77149-143-3

A. Read the story. Then check ✔ the true sentences.

Camping *Fun*

Jason and his family are going camping this weekend. They will go to a lake up north. Jason likes to go there. They go there every year. There is just so much to do. He can swim with his parents, catch some fish, and explore the woods nearby. They will sleep in a big tent. It is a new tent that his dad bought for the trip. Their old one is broken.

1. Jason will play baseball with his dad and mom. ◯

2. Jason likes camping by the lake. ◯

3. Jason will sleep in the old tent. ◯

4. Jason can go fishing. ◯

5. Jason's father bought a new tent for the camping trip. ◯

6. Jason and his family go camping by the lake every year. ◯

ISBN: 978-1-77149-143-3

B. Check ✔ the things on the list that Jason needs for the trip. Then suggest one more thing he should take and answer the question.

1. ## Packing List for Camping

(A) water

(B) vase   (C) sunscreen

(D) flashlight   (E) swimwear

(F) cap   (G) microwave

(H) compass   (I) garbage can

(J) piano   (K) insect repellent

(L) map   (✔) _____

2. Why must a tent be waterproof to be used for camping?

_____

_____

71

ISBN: 978-1-77149-143-3

C. Match each word with its opposite.

night	little	cold	in
sad	light	up	

Words that have opposite meanings are called antonyms.

1. big _____

2. down _____

3. heavy _____

4. day _____

5. out _____

6. happy _____

7. hot _____

big

small

8. Choose three pairs of opposite words from above. Use each pair in a sentence of your own.

The squirrel is climbing **up** and **down** the tree.

- _____

- _____

- _____

ISBN: 978-1-77149-143-3

Week

6

A

English

D. Circle the following camping words in the word search.

tent   pillow   marshmallow   flashlight   fire
hot dog   campground   canoe   logs
mosquito   journal   matches

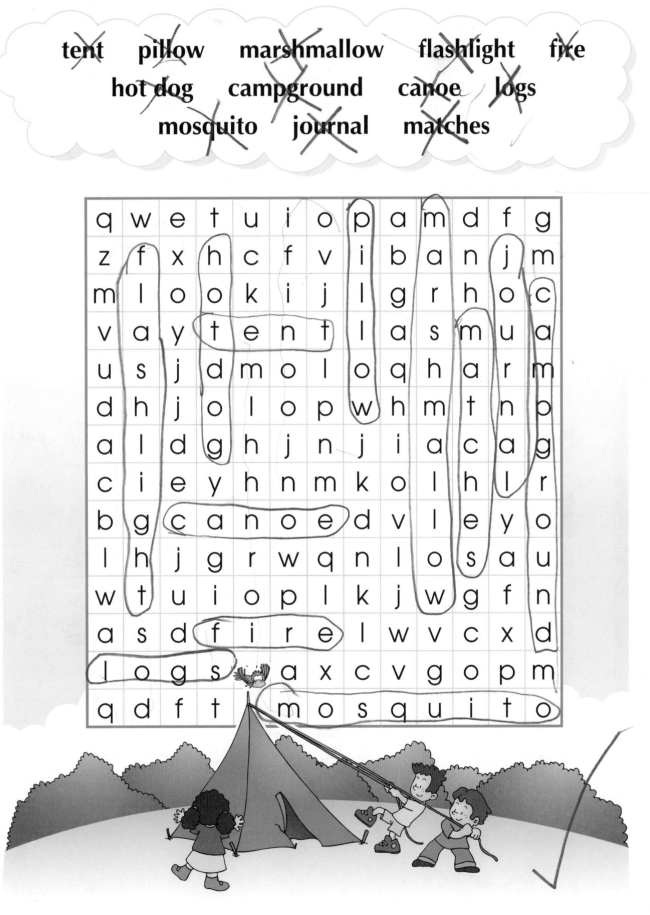

ISBN: 978-1-77149-143-3   *Grades 1-2*

A. Colour the containers.

more than 1 cup: **red**
less than 1 cup: **blue**

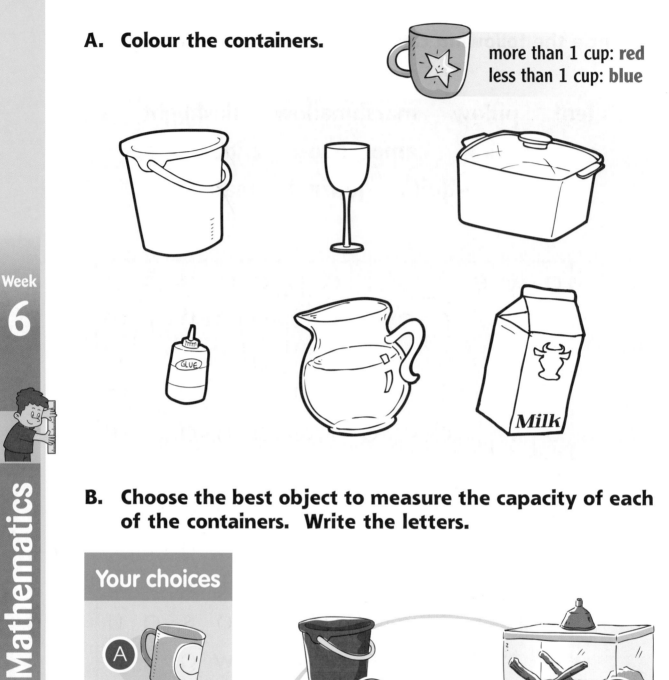

B. Choose the best object to measure the capacity of each of the containers. Write the letters.

Your choices

A

B

C

ISBN: 978-1-77149-143-3

C. See how many cups of water each container can hold. Solve the problems.

1. How many cups of water can

    a. a pot hold?   _____ cups

    b. a bottle hold?   _____ cups

2. Which container has

    a. the greatest capacity?   _____

    b. the least capacity?   _____

3. How many pots of water are needed to fill a pail?

    _____ pots

4. If the jug is half-filled with water, how many more cups of water are needed to fill up the jug?

    _____ more

ISBN: 978-1-77149-143-3

D. Look at the graph. Then answer the questions.

Number of Glasses of
Water the Containers Hold

jug

kettle

tank

mug

bottle

1. Which container, a bottle or a mug, has a greater capacity?

   _____

2. How many glasses of water can

   a. a kettle hold?   _____ glasses

   b. a tank and a kettle hold?   _____ glasses

3. Which of the containers above is best for measuring the capacity of a bathtub?

   _____

Mathematics

ISBN: 978-1-77149-143-3

E. Colour the container that can be traced to get each shape.

ISBN: 978-1-77149-143-3

A. Match the tool with the thing(s) that the tool can hold.

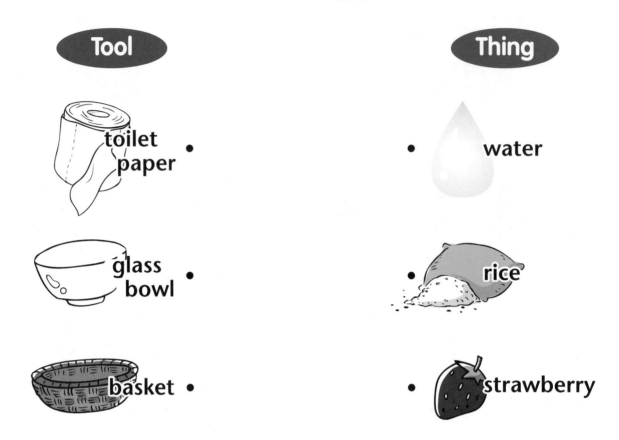

Tool

- toilet paper
- glass bowl
- basket

Thing

- water
- rice
- strawberry

B. List the solid items in the mixing bowl and the liquid items in the measuring cup.

cheese   Oil   Sugar REFINED 1kg   Milk   Juice   Flour

Science

ISBN: 978-1-77149-143-3

C. **Determine whether the water in each picture is "solid" or "liquid". Then fill in the blanks.**

melts   freezes   water   ice

1.

_____   _____

The water _____ and becomes _____ .

2.

_____   _____

The ice _____ and becomes _____ .

ISBN: 978-1-77149-143-3

A. Trace to see the different types of homes of people from different countries. Then circle the correct words to describe their homes.

I live in a yurt which is easy to make in the desert of Mongolia.

yurt
South Gobi Desert, Mongolia

cone-shaped / round roof

round / square tent

small / large door in the centre

I like living in an igloo in the snowy land of Arctic Canada.

igloo
Nunavut, Canada

shaped like a **dome / cube**

made of blocks of **ice / wood**

large / small opening in the centre

ISBN: 978-1-77149-143-3

Social Studies

B. **People around the world play different sports. Check ✔ the popular sports in different areas. Then draw a popular sport that people play in your area.**

Britain has sunny summers and lush grassland.

Quebec, Canada has cold, snowy winters and gently sloping hills.

A Popular Sport in My Area

ISBN: 978-1-77149-143-3

ISBN: 978-1-77149-143-3

WEEK 7

English

- read a recipe and answer questions
- read and draw
- compare and contrast two things

Mathematics

- count coins
- write times
- do the counting
- draw and name shapes

Science

- identify suitable seasonal clothing
- learn about the yearly seasonal cycle

Social Studies

- identify natural resources
- learn about ways to save resources

Week 7

* The Canadian penny is no longer in circulation. It is used in the unit to show money amounts to the cent.

ISBN: 978-1-77149-143-3

A. Read the recipe for making sugar cookies.

Sugar Cookies

Ingredients:

- $\frac{3}{4}$ cup of softened butter
- 1 cup of white sugar
- 2 eggs
- $\frac{1}{2}$ teaspoon of vanilla extract
- $2\frac{1}{2}$ cups of flour
- 3 teaspoons of milk
- 1 teaspoon of baking powder
- $\frac{1}{2}$ teaspoon of salt

Directions:

1. In a large bowl, mix the butter, milk, and sugar until the mixture is smooth. Beat in the eggs and the vanilla extract.

2. Stir in the flour, baking powder, and salt.

3. Cover and chill the dough in the refrigerator for one hour.

4. Roll out the dough on a floured surface. Cut into shapes with cookie cutters. Place cookies on an ungreased cookie sheet.

5. Bake 6 to 8 minutes in a heated oven. Cool completely.

ISBN: 978-1-77149-143-3

B.   Check ✔ the ingredients for making sugar cookies.

salt   pepper

flour   vanilla extract

sugar   chocolate chips

C.   Give short answers to the following questions.

1.   Which three things do you mix together first?

   _____

2.   How long does it take to chill the dough?

   _____

3.   What can you use to cut the dough into shapes?

   _____

4.   Where should you place the cookies to bake them?

   _____

5.   How long does it take to bake the cookies?

   _____

ISBN: 978-1-77149-143-3   *Grades 1-2*

D. Read, draw, and colour.

1. Draw some cookies on the plate.
2. Draw some apples in the tree.
3. Add a star on the back of the chair.
4. Draw a flower in the picture frame.
5. Colour the picture.

English

ISBN: 978-1-77149-143-3

E. Match the animals with what they say about themselves. Then complete the sentences.

1.

- "I can be a pet."
- "I have fur."
- "I bark."
- "I have a tail."
- "I chase mice."
- "I purr."

When we compare two things, we think about how they are the same. When we contrast two things, we think about how they are different.

2. Dogs and cats are the same because

_____

_____

3. Dogs and cats are different because

_____

_____

ISBN: 978-1-77149-143-3

A. Write the cost of each item. Then check ✔ the correct number of coins to answer each question.

1. [_____] ¢

2. [_____] ¢

3. [_____] ¢

4. [_____] ¢

5. Sue pays [10 CENTS] for a [item]. What is her change?

6. Ben buys 1 [hat] and 1 [octopus]. How much does he pay?

ISBN: 978-1-77149-143-3

B. Write the times. Then put the events in order.

Events in Order (1-4)

_____ o'clock

☐

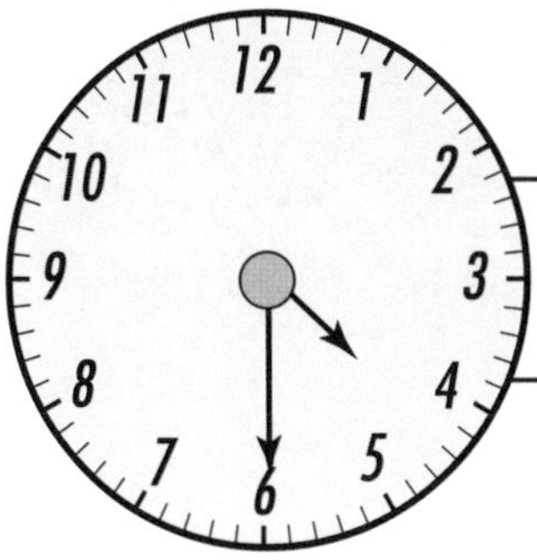

half past _____

☐

_____

☐

_____

☐

ISBN: 978-1-77149-143-3

Mathematics

C. Count and write the numbers to complete the sentences.

1. There are _____ ducks on the log.

2. _____ duck is standing on a rock.

3. _____ ducks are swimming.

4. There are _____ ducks in all.

5. There is a total of _____ flowers.

6. _____ of the flowers are yellow.

7. There are _____ butterflies.

8. There are _____ clouds in the sky.

ISBN: 978-1-77149-143-3

D. **Trace the dotted lines to draw each shape. Then redraw the shape next to it and name the shape.**

This is a 1._____

2._____

3._____

ISBN: 978-1-77149-143-3

A. Name the season shown in each picture. Then colour the suitable clothing for the season.

spring   summer   fall   winter

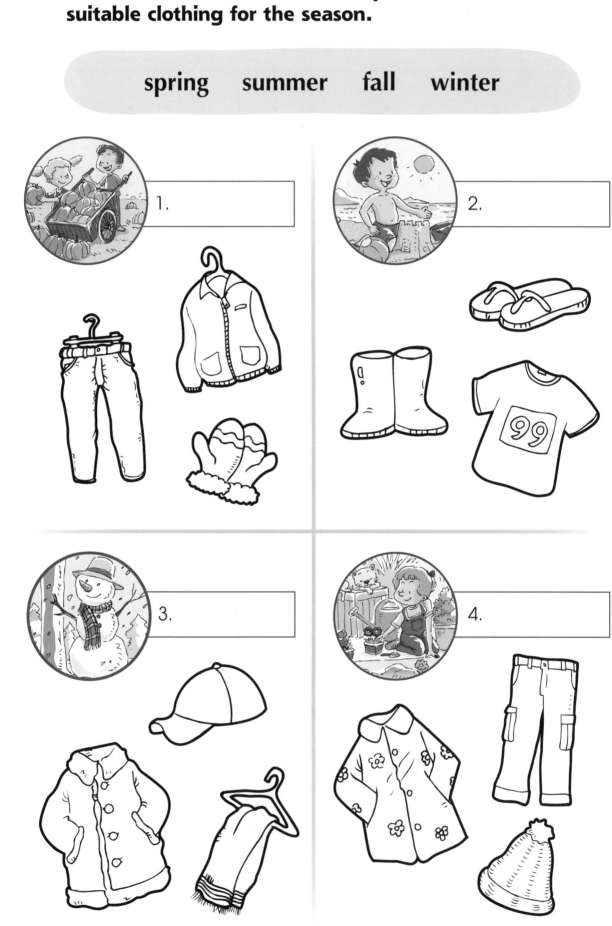

1.

2.

3.

4.

ISBN: 978-1-77149-143-3

B. Fill in the blanks. Then trace the arrows and name the seasons.

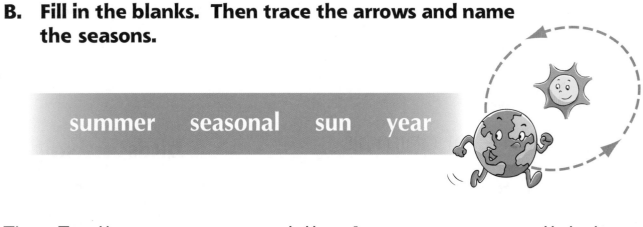

| summer | seasonal | sun | year |

The Earth goes around the 1._____ . It takes the Earth about one 2._____ to go around the sun once. It is this trip that gives us the yearly 3._____ cycle with the four seasons in Canada: spring, 4._____ , fall, and winter.

The Seasonal Cycle

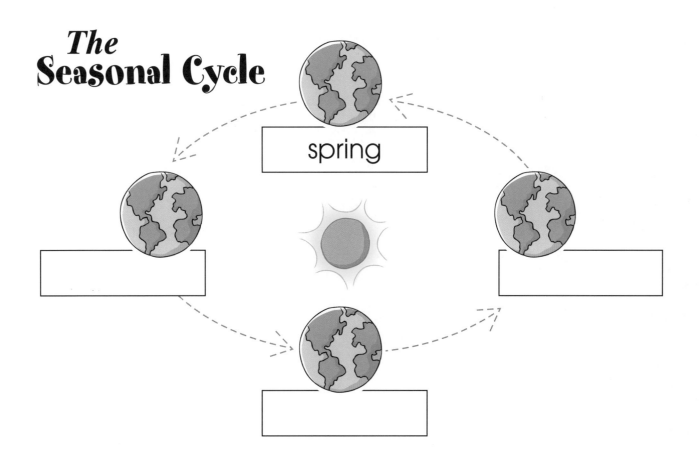

spring

ISBN: 978-1-77149-143-3

A. Look at the picture. Write about the natural resources with the help of the given words.

Forest

- home of animals

  and _____

- natural resource:

  _____

birds	soil
fish	water
plants	wood

Tree

- home of _____

- natural resource:

  _____

River

- home of _____

- natural resource:

  _____

Natural Resources

ISBN: 978-1-77149-143-3

B. **Circle the correct words to see in what ways we can save resources.**

 **Ways to Save Resources**

1.  Turn **on / off** the lights when you leave a room.

2. **Don't / Do** let the water run while brushing your teeth.

3. Don't leave the refrigerator door **open / closed** .

4. **Throw away / Recycle** paper, plastic, glass bottles, and aluminum cans.

5. **Bring / Forget** your own reusable bag when you go shopping.

There are many things that we can do to save resources. Can you come up with one more idea and share it with your parents?

ISBN: 978-1-77149-143-3 *Grades 1-2*

ISBN: 978-1-77149-143-3

WEEK 8

Arts & Crafts
- make binoculars

Comics
- Sam's Birthday Surprise

Fun Places to Go in Summer
- Toronto's Waterfront

ISBN: 978-1-77149-143-3

Week 8

Arts & Crafts

Materials:

- 2 toilet paper rolls
- single hole punch
- glue
- paint
- string

ISBN: 978-1-77149-143-3

Binoculars

1.

2.

3.

4.

Directions:

1. Paint and draw some patterns on paper rolls. Let them dry.

2. Glue rolls together on sides.

3. Punch holes in sides of rolls.

4. Tie string through the holes.

ISBN: 978-1-77149-143-3

Sam's Birthday Surprise

It was Sam's birthday. His parents gave him an alien spaceship as a gift. Sam loved it. He loves aliens.

Thank you, Mommy and Daddy!

Sam got on the school bus. His friends wished him a "happy birthday".

We have a surprise for you. But you'll have to wait.

During lunchtime, Sam's friends were busy preparing a party for Sam.

Do you think we have enough table tennis balls?

ISBN: 978-1-77149-143-3

They cut holes in some boxes. Then they painted the boxes.

Sam did not notice any of this. He was busy playing with his spaceship.

Suddenly, Sam returned to the classroom. His friends quickly hid everything.

Weee...beep beep!

After school, Sam realized that the school bus was emptier than usual. But he did not think too much about it. He continued to play with his new spaceship.

ISBN: 978-1-77149-143-3

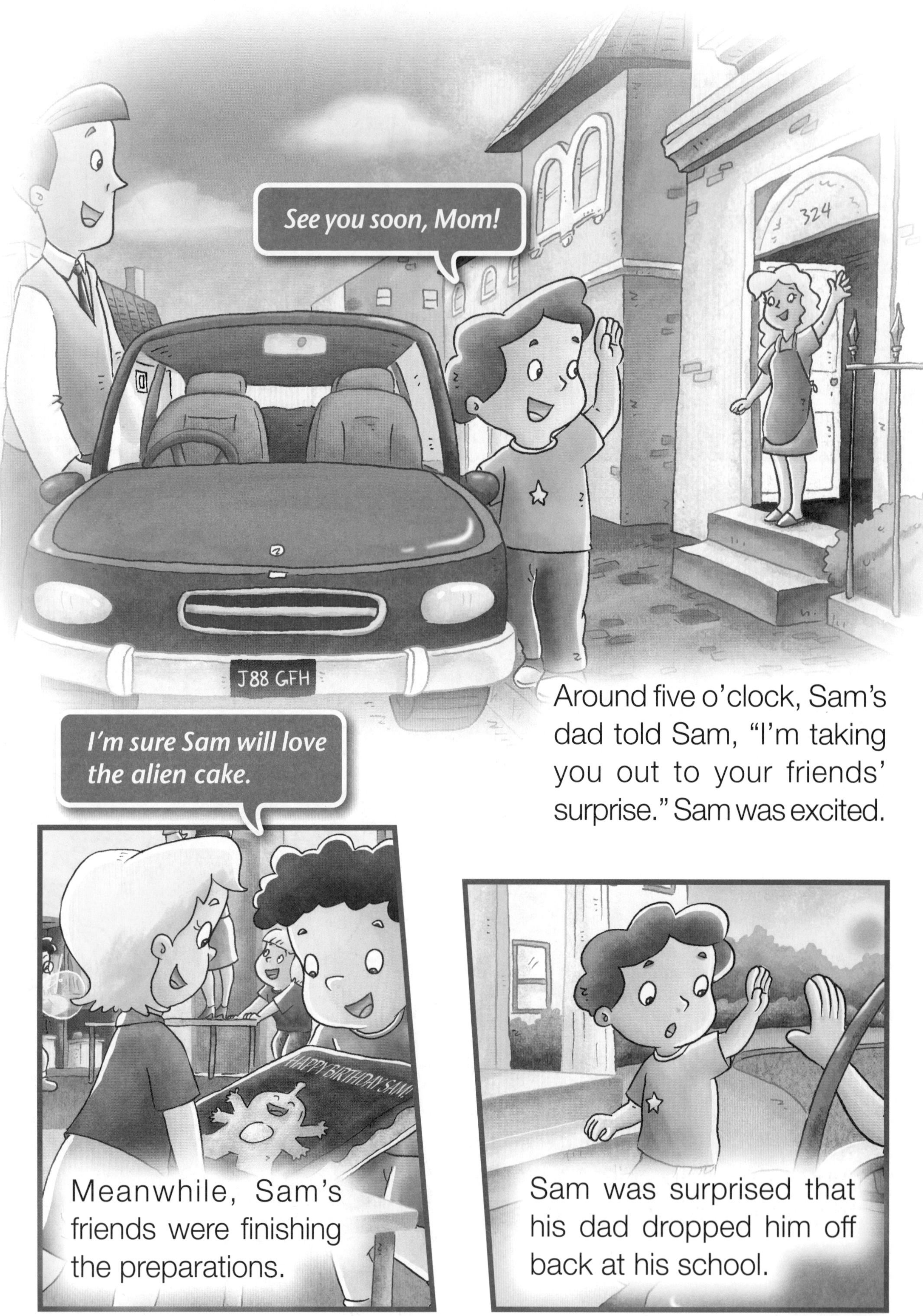

See you soon, Mom!

I'm sure Sam will love the alien cake.

Around five o'clock, Sam's dad told Sam, "I'm taking you out to your friends' surprise." Sam was excited.

Meanwhile, Sam's friends were finishing the preparations.

Sam was surprised that his dad dropped him off back at his school.

ISBN: 978-1-77149-143-3

Sam opened the door...

Surprise!

They all looked like aliens. It was an alien birthday party!

Make a wish!

And blow out the candles!

Sam put on an alien outfit too. They played party games and ate the alien cake. Sam's birthday party was a perfect surprise!

The End

103

Toronto's
Waterfront

Taking a leisurely walk along the boardwalk, playing volleyball on the beach, and enjoying the beautiful view of Lake Ontario – are these the only things you can do at Toronto's waterfront? Of course not! You can also have great fun at Harbourfront Centre, which is Canada's leading centre for the arts and culture.

A series of festivals are held there each weekend during the summer. You can learn different dance styles, make your own musical instrument and play music with it, create your own hand puppet and put on a puppet show on the outdoor stage, and even learn to be a ringmaster or a circus performer.

Get outside and heat up your summer fun with singing, dancing, games, and more!

ISBN: 978-1-77149-143-3

Answers
Grades 1-2

Credits
Photos ("children" Gennadiy Poznyakov/123RF.com, "beach" Alexandr Ozerov/123RF.com)

ISBN: 978-1-77149-143-3

Week 1

English

A. 1. fun   2. flew
   3. days   4. school
   5. friends   6. till
   7. end   8. We

B. 1. baseball   2. biking
   3. boating   4. camping
   5. fishing   6. hiking
   7. rollerblading   8. soccer
   9. swimming   10. tennis

C.

b	u	s	s	o	c	c	e	r	g	s	r
i	e	t	w	j	l	r	c	l	e	m	o
k	h	f	i	s	h	i	n	g	p	q	l
i	g	j	m	b	a	s	e	b	a	l	l
n	i	o	m	v	i	p	a	l	r	s	e
g	q	i	i	e	j	o	s	c	h	s	r
t	e	n	n	i	s	u	d	a	z	d	b
p	k	v	g	l	e	y	f	m	x	f	l
r	h	s	e	p	q	t	g	p	c	g	a
t	f	t	u	t	a	r	j	i	v	y	d
h	i	k	i	n	g	e	k	n	b	k	i
y	w	k	s	o	c	w	l	g	n	o	n
c	d	b	o	a	t	i	n	g	m	v	g

D. (Individual writing and drawing)

Mathematics

A. 1. 23 ; 23 ; B   2. 32 ; 32 ; B
B. 1. 7   2. 4
   3. 10   4. 8
   5. 6 + 6 ; 12 ; 12   6. 7 + 8 ; 15 ; 15

C.

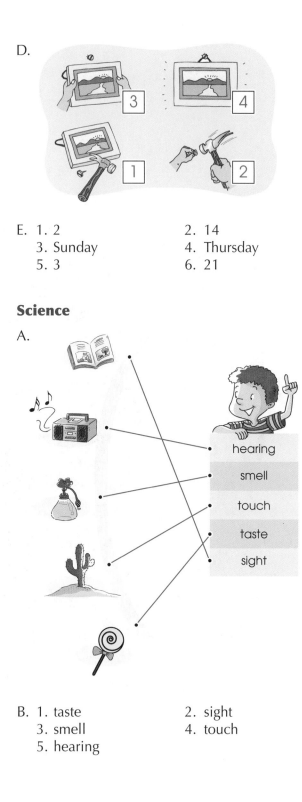

D.

E. 1. 2   2. 14
   3. Sunday   4. Thursday
   5. 3   6. 21

Science

A.

B. 1. taste   2. sight
   3. smell   4. touch
   5. hearing

ISBN: 978-1-77149-143-3

Social Studies

(Individual drawing and answers)

Week 2
English

A. 1. at 9:00 a.m.
   2. at 3:00 p.m.
   3. on Saturday and Sunday
   4. toys, clothes, furniture, and comic books
B. Furniture:
   chair ; desk ; couch ; table ; bed
   Toy:
   doll ; teddy bear ; baseball ; skipping rope ;
   jigsaw puzzle
   Clothing:
   pants ; coat ; dress ; hat ; scarf
C. 1. . ; .   2. ? ; !
   3. !
D. duck ; pan ; cup ; book ; lamp ; pig
   kite ; sun ; hair ; bike

Mathematics

A. A: square   B: triangle
   C: rectangle   D: rectangle
   E: circle   F: triangle
B. square: 3
   triangle: 4
   rectangle: 9
   circle: 5
C. 1.

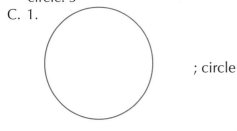

; circle

2.

; triangle

3.

; rectangle

4.

; square

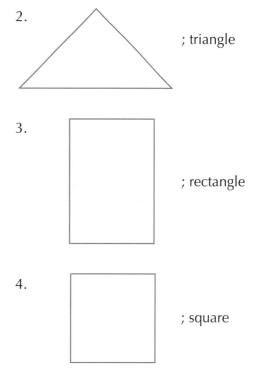

D. (Individual colouring)

E. 1. longer ; over   2. bigger ; under
   3. right ; bigger   4. A ; B

ISBN: 978-1-77149-143-3

ANSWERS

Science

A. In the forest: fox ; bear
   In the river: shrimp ; fish
   In the tree: bird ; squirrel

B.

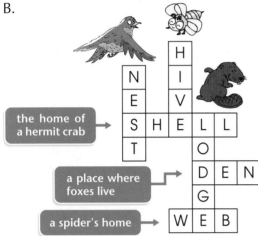

Social Studies

A.

B. (Individual drawing and answers)

Week 3

English

A. 1. at his neighbour's garage sale
   2. one dollar
   3. in his backyard
   4. robins, bluebirds, and cardinals

B. 1. Bob found a treasure.
   2. Bob bought the bird bath.
   3. Bob put the bird bath in the backyard.
   4. He filled the bath with water.
   5. The sun warmed the water.
C. 1. outside   2. backyard
   3. afternoon   4. bluebirds
D. newspaper ; pancake ; mailbox ; goldfish ;
   football ; watermelon ; butterfly ; cupboard
E. 1. A SWALLOW   2. CRACKERS
   3. A BLUEBIRD

Mathematics

A. 1. sphere   2. cone
   3. cube   4. cylinder
B. D ; C ; B ; A
   A ; B ; D ; C
C. 1. on ; in front of ; beside
   2. inside ; beside ; under
   3. over ; between ; behind
D. 1.

   2.

E. Check: C, D
F. 1.

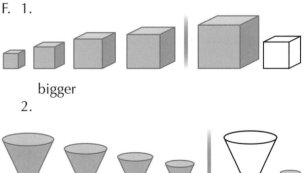

   bigger
   2.

   lower

ISBN: 978-1-77149-143-3

Science

A.
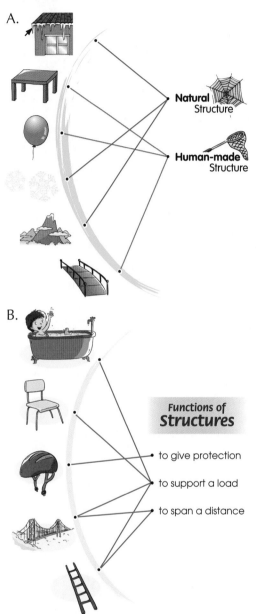

B.

Social Studies

A. 1. China ; turnip cakes
   2. India ; samosas
B. (Individual drawing and writing)

Week 5

English

A. 1. picking   2. baskets
   3. trunk   4. rows
   5. red   6. mouth
   7. sweet
B. (Draw lines through these sentences.)
   1. There was a robin in the sky.
   2. Jan and Ted enjoy riding their bikes with Aunt Mary.
   3. Grapes are purple in colour.
   4. Cherries are red too.
   5. I can make baskets.
C. (Individual drawing and writing)
D. 1. sk ; skates   2. sp ; spider
   3. pl ; plane   4. cl ; clown
   5. fl ; flag   6. gr ; grapes
   7. fl ; flower   8. st ; star

Mathematics

A. 1. never

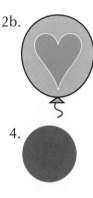

2a.   2b.

3. always   4.

B. 1. 13 ;

$$\begin{array}{r} 6 \\ +\ 7 \\ \hline 1\ 3 \end{array}$$

2. 12 ;

$$\begin{array}{r} 4 \\ +\ 8 \\ \hline 1\ 2 \end{array}$$

3. 7 ;

$$\begin{array}{r} 1\ 6 \\ -\ 9 \\ \hline 7 \end{array}$$

ISBN: 978-1-77149-143-3

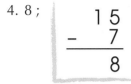
4. 8 ;

$$\begin{array}{r} 15 \\ -\ \ 7 \\ \hline 8 \end{array}$$

C. tigers: 3 ; giraffes: 50 ;
   raccoons: 42 ; geese: 79
D. 1. 46 ; 50 ; 52 ; 56
   2. 45 ; 50 ; 60
E. 1. circle ; 4   2. triangle ; 2
   3. square ; 3   4. rectangle ; 3

Science

A. iron: B, D
   cloth: E, I
   glass: G, H
   feather: A, F
   wood: C, J
B. 1. grow ; move
   2. change ; think

Social Studies

A. 1.

North Pole

Northern Hemisphere

Canada

Mexico

Brazil

Equator

Chile

South Pole

Southern Hemisphere

2. Northern Hemisphere
3. Southern Hemisphere.

B.

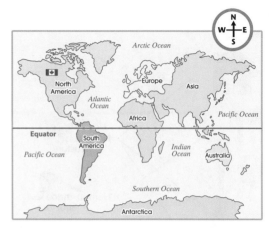

North America
The Seven Continents: North America ; South
America ; Europe ; Asia ; Africa ; Australia ;
Antarctica
The Five Oceans: Arctic Ocean ; Atlantic Ocean ;
Pacific Ocean ; Indian Ocean ; Southern Ocean

Week 6

English

A. Check: 2, 4, 5, 6
B. 1. Check: A, C, D, E, F, H, K, L
      (Suggested answer) sleeping bag
   2. You do not want to get wet inside the tent if
      it rains.
C. 1. little   2. up
   3. light   4. night
   5. in   6. sad
   7. cold
   8. (Individual writing)
D.

ISBN: 978-1-77149-143-3

Mathematics

A.

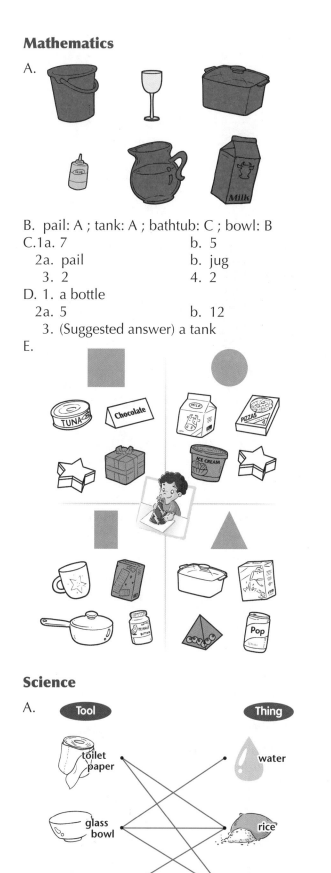

B. pail: A ; tank: A ; bathtub: C ; bowl: B

C. 1a. 7   b. 5
  2a. pail   b. jug
  3. 2   4. 2

D. 1. a bottle
  2a. 5   b. 12
  3. (Suggested answer) a tank

E.

Science

A.

B. Solid: cheese ; sugar ; flour
    Liquid: oil ; milk ; juice

C. 1. liquid ; solid
      freezes ; ice
   2. solid ; liquid
      melts ; water

Social Studies

A.

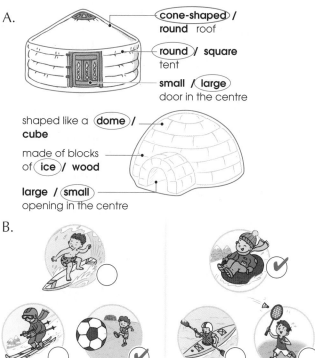

cone-shaped / round roof

round / square tent

small / large door in the centre

shaped like a dome / cube

made of blocks of ice / wood

large / small opening in the centre

B.

(Individual drawing)

Week 7

English

B. Check: milk, butter, eggs, salt, flour, vanilla extract, sugar

C. 1. butter, milk, and sugar
   2. one hour
   3. cookie cutters
   4. on an ungreased cookie sheet
   5. six to eight minutes

ISBN: 978-1-77149-143-3

D. (Individual colouring)

E. 1.

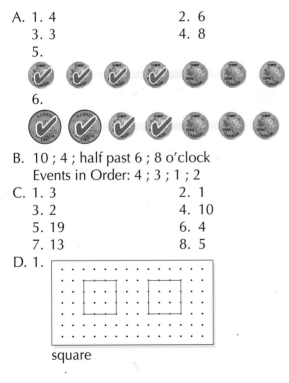

"I can be a pet."
"I have fur."
"I bark."
"I have a tail."
"I chase mice."
"I purr."

2. they can be pets, they have fur, and they have a tail.
3. dogs bark but cats purr, and cats chase mice.

Mathematics

A. 1. 4   2. 6
   3. 3   4. 8
   5.
   6.

B. 10 ; 4 ; half past 6 ; 8 o'clock
   Events in Order: 4 ; 3 ; 1 ; 2

C. 1. 3   2. 1
   3. 2   4. 10
   5. 19   6. 4
   7. 13   8. 5

D. 1.

square

2.   3.

rectangle   triangle

Science

A. 1. fall   2. summer

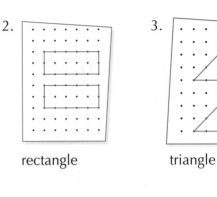

   3. winter   4. spring

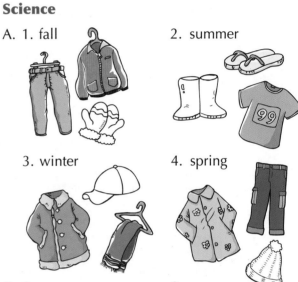

B. 1. sun   2. year
   3. seasonal   4. summer

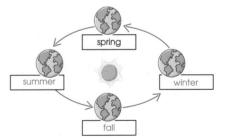

Social Studies

A. Forest: plants ; soil
   Tree: birds ; wood
   River: fish ; water

B. 1. off   2. Don't
   3. open   4. Recycle
   5. Bring

ISBN: 978-1-77149-143-3